Saints Alive!

by Jack Hamm

KREGEL PUBLICATIONS
Grand Rapids 6, Michigan

"THERE WAS A MAN THERE WHO MADE AN ALL-DAY SPEECH. I FORGOT HIS NAME, BUT I THINK HE WAS AN ESCAPED MISSIONARY."

"WHY DO THEY CLOSE CHURCH AND SUNDAY
SCHOOL EVERY TIME WE HAVE WEEKEND
COMPANY ?"

"I DON'T BELIEVE MY DADDY WILL BE IN HEAVEN...HE COULDN'T LEAVE THE STORE"

"WHILE I THINK OF IT, JENKINS, PLEASE TIGHTEN THE LIGHT BULBS OVER THE CHOIR LOFT"

"THE CREATOR MUST HAVE HAD A SENSE OF HUMOR WHEN HE MADE ALL THOSE ODD-BALL LOOKING HUMANS"

"HOW DID IT HAPPEN ? OH, THEY ALL TRIED TO GET IN THE BACK PEW"

"THE DOG? DON'T WORRY ABOUT HIM, PARSON...NEVER BITES ANYONE UNLESS HE'S A SCOUNDREL."

"WE DON'T TAKE ANYTHING BUT THE LIGHT BILL "

"WOULD THOSE WHO ARE IN THE HABIT OF
PUTTING BUTTONS IN THE COLLECTION PLATE
KINDLY USE THEIR OWN BUTTONS AND NOT
THOSE ON THE PEW CUSHIONS"

"A 'SAINT' BERNARD YOU SAY... PAYING
AN ECCLESIASTICAL CALL NO DOUBT...
PLEASE SHOW HIM IN, GRISWOLD "

"MY EYE SIGHT HAS BEEN A MITE POOR OF LATE AND I LIKE TO NEVER FOUND THE CHURCH HOUSE... ANYWAY, AS VISITING PASTOR, I THANK YOU... "

"REMEMBER, THE PASTOR SAID WE SHOULD NOT 'BEAR FALSE WITNESS AGAINST OUR NEIGHBOR', SO BEFORE YOU TELL MRS. JONES, ASK MRS. BROWN WHERE MRS. SMITH HEARD ABOUT MRS. GREEN"

"YOU HAVE NO IDEA WHAT YOUR SERMONS MEAN TO MY HUSBAND SINCE HE'S LOST HIS MIND"

"I RECOGNIZE YOU, McDUFF, THE SERVICE STARTS IN TWENTY MINUTES"

"AFTERALL, MINE IS NEW AND I'M PROUD OF IT TOO "

"I'VE COMPLETELY FORGOTTEN THE NAME, BUT THE SNORE WAS FAMILIAR"

" I LOVE TO HEAR YOU PREACH. YOU GET SO MANY THINGS OUT OF YOUR TEXT THAT ARE REALLY NOT THERE "

"NO ONE SPOKE TO ME ... THAT'S THE COLDEST CHURCH I WAS EVER IN"

"ALWAYS CLAIMS HE'S MEDITATING...
NEVER SEES THE PLATE GO BY"

"WHAT DENOMINATION ? WELL, MOTHER GOES TO THE CENTRAL CHURCH AND FATHER TO THE COMMUNITY CHURCH ... AS FOR ME, I'M RADIO "

" I DON'T KNOW... SHE JUST SAYS SHE
ALWAYS SINGS BETTER IN THE SHOWER"

"REMEMBER OUR DEAL, HARRIGAN, WE SPLIT THE RICE AFTER THIS EVENING'S WEDDING"

"IT'S NOT THE SPIRIT OF THE GIFT I WISH TO QUESTION, IT'S... WELL, REGARDING YOUR BUSINESS OF COUNTERFEITING"

"WHEN YOU SAY, 'WHO'LL BE THE FIRST TO RISE THEREBY INDICATING A PLEDGE OF $5,000,' ALL YOU HAVE TO DO IS THROW SWITCH 'A' CONNECTING SEAT 'B'."

"SURE ENOUGH ... REV. FLUG *DID* DROP
SEEDS IN THE DUST ON OUR BIBLE.'"

"OH, OH! LITTLE DO THEY REALIZE HOW
WELL ILLUSTRATED THE SERMON WILL
BE TODAY"

"NOT SO REVERENT, BUT IT SURE
REGAINS THEIR ATTENTION"

"I NOTICE IN THE AGE OF COMPACT CARS YOU'VE GIVEN A COMPACT OFFERING."

"THOUGH IT WILL COME AS A SURPRISE TO HIM, A SPECIAL COMMITTEE VOTED TO GIVE THE PASTOR A RAISE."

"'SILVER AND GOLD HAVE I NONE', DECLARED SIMON PETER TO THE LAME MAN AT THE GATE OF THE TEMPLE. WHAT FURTHER PROOF IS NEEDED THAT PETER WAS A PREACHER?"

"SOMETIMES HUBERT GETS THE NOTION THAT REV. RIPPLE IS REFERRING TO HIM IN HIS SIN SERMONS"

"HMMM ... WONDER IF REV. BIFBY'S HEAD IS FULL OF HIS SUBJECT... I SEE TODAY HIS TOPIC IS 'SPACE'."

"I CAN'T UNDERSTAND IT...THIS IS THE FIRST
TIME PATRICIA HAS GONE TO THE NURSERY
WITHOUT CRYING"

"OH DEAR ... I ACCIDENTALLY SENT THE BUTCHER'S $12.00 DOG FOOD CHECK IN PLACE OF OUR $2.00 CHURCH PLEDGE."

" THE REVEREND DR. JOSHKINS WILL
LECTURE ON 'FOOLS' IN THE CENTRAL
AVENUE CHURCH MONDAY EVENING, AND
I TRUST A GREAT MANY WILL ATTEND"

"ALL RIGHT! WHO WAS THE WISE GUY THAT CHANGED 'COUNT YOUR BLESSINGS' TO 'COUNT YOUR CALORIES'?"

"YUP, PARSON, MY MAMA SAYS MY PRAYERS
FOR ME EVERY NIGHT. SHE SAYS, 'THANK
HEAVENS YOU'RE IN BED!'"

"AS THE BACK ROW FILLS UP PASTOR PEAK PUSHES A BUTTON THAT MOVES IT DOWN FRONT"

"THIS EXPLAINS THE MISPLACED HIGH
NOTE WE HEARD IN LAST SUNDAY'S
HYMN...THESE TWO BOARDS PINCH
WHERE THEY COME TOGETHER"

"THE COTTON ? OH, HE NEVER LIKES TO
HEAR HIS REPEAT SERMONS A SECOND
TIME "

"HE WAS A STRANGER AND I TOOK
HIM IN"

"HE WAS ASLEEP WHEN THE MISSIONARY SPEAKER WAS BROUGHT ON "

"THE CENTER, GUARDS, TACKLES AND ENDS ARE SINGING WELL ... NOW, CONCERNING THE BACKFIELD..."

"THE OFFERINGS MUST BE LOW AGAIN...
THERE GOES REV. RIPPLE WITH HIS GUM
ON A STICK ROUTINE."

"OH STOP CARVING A NOTCH EVERY TIME HE SAYS 'IN CONCLUSION'!"

"REGARDING THE REFRESHMENTS FOR THE
CHURCH SOCIAL, LADIES, WHAT WE WANT
ARE NOT ABSTRACT PROMISES, BUT
CONCRETE CAKE "

"THAT'S THE BEST 'PEACE OF MIND' SERMON I'VE HEARD IN A LONG TIME"

"EVEN IF IT WAS A MIS-FIRE, THE PUBLICITY OF HAVING OUR PREACHER IN ORBIT SHOULD DO THE CAPE CANAVERAL CHURCH A LOT OF GOOD"

"OFF THE CUFF LET ME SAY THE SWAB IS
PAYING ME EXACTLY NOTHING AS HIS
PULPIT SUPPLY"

"SPEND MONEY ON THE OLD BELFRY? BAH!
WHAT WAS GOOD ENOUGH FOR MY FATHER
IS GOOD ENOUGH FOR ME...."

"JUST A MINUTE, THORNDYKE!"

"I HAD IT PAINTED TO STOP ALL THIS CHIT-CHAT BEFORE THE SERVICE"

"JUNIOR, YOU WIGGLED! YOU'RE DIS-
TURBING THE SERVICE!"

"IN FACT AS A YOUNG COUNTRY PREACHER
I ATE SO MUCH OF IT FRIED, FOR AWHILE
I THOUGHT I MIGHT TURN INTO ONE"

"BEFORE THE SERVICE I HAD A CONFER-
ENCE WITH MY WIFE ... AND, BY THE WAY,
LET ME SAY I AM DEFINITELY AGAINST
WOMEN'S POINTED-TOE SHOES "

"OH DEAR! IT LOOKS LIKE JUXTON HAD ANOTHER ACCIDENT COMING DOWN AISLE FIVE"

"I HARDLY THINK THAT'S WHAT WAS MEANT BY AN 'ADEQUATE FOLLOW-UP IN OUR FINANCIAL CAMPAIGN'"

"THIS MODEL IS CALLED 'THE LOST HALF HOUR' ... THE BACK RECLINES AND THE FOAM RUBBER IS SIX INCHES THICK"

"OH DEAR... HERE IT COMES.' DEACON SMITHERS IS DETERMINED TO CURE MR. FIGBY OF SLEEPING IN CHURCH. "

"MAN! THAT WAS NOTHING BUT A COOL SERMON, DADDIO!"

"I'M GOING TO SLIP OUT... HE'S PREACHED
TWELVE MINUTES OVERTIME NOW"